student
WORKBOOK

AQA (A)

AS Psychology
Cognitive & Developmental Psychology
Molly Marshall

Philip Allan Updates
Market Place, Deddington, Oxfordshire OX15 0SE
tel: 01869 338652, fax: 01869 337590
e-mail: sales@philipallan.co.uk
www.philipallan.co.uk

© Philip Allan Updates 2004

ISBN 1 84489 115 1

Printed by Raithby, Lawrence & Co. Ltd, Leicester

Environmental information
The paper on which this title is printed is sourced
from managed, sustainable forests.

Introduction

The aim of this workbook is to help you to increase your understanding of cognitive and developmental psychology and to improve your skills in answering the types of question you might encounter in the AQA (A) AS examination.

The workbook includes a variety of stimulus material that will help you to learn about psychological research, terminology and concepts. The questions are wide-ranging and designed to support you as you develop skills of analysis, interpretation and evaluation. Writing answers to the questions will help you learn to communicate your knowledge and understanding of psychology in a clear and effective manner. The questions are organised so that they become progressively more difficult within each topic. As you complete the workbook, you should become confident that you are learning the content required in the exam and how to write effective answers that will achieve high marks.

The workbook is organised into two sections:

Section 1: Cognitive psychology

This section comprises four topics. Topic 1 focuses on research into the nature and structure of memory, including encoding, capacity and duration of short-term memory (STM) and long-term memory (LTM). Topic 2 focuses on models of memory, and includes the multi-store model of memory, working memory and levels of processing. Topic 3 focuses on forgetting, and includes explanations of forgetting in STM and LTM as well as research into the role of emotional factors. Topic 4 focuses on eyewitness testimony, including reconstructive memory and the role of leading questions.

Section 2: Developmental psychology

This section comprises five topics. Topic 1 focuses on the development and variety of infant attachments. Topic 2 focuses on research into individual differences, including secure and insecure attachments and cross-cultural variations. Topic 3 focuses on psychological explanations of attachment and includes learning theory and Bowlby's theory. Topic 4 focuses on research into the effects of deprivation and privation. Topic 5 looks at the issue of daycare and includes research into the effects of daycare on children's cognitive and social development.

When using this workbook you can study either the cognitive or the developmental section first. To gain maximum benefit, within each section you should complete the topics and questions in the order given. There are several ways in which you can use this workbook:

(1) As an integral part of your learning experience to be used in conjunction with your class notes, handouts and textbook. Periodically, your teacher might ask you to hand your book in for assessment.

(2) As a revision tool, in which case you should work through the topics, writing the answers as practice for the exam.

(3) As a combination of **(1)** and **(2)** — if, as you progress through the module, you write answers to all the questions in this book, at the end of the course you will have created a valuable resource from which to revise!

Whichever way you choose, we hope this workbook will help you in your studies and in your exam.

Can you remember what you did yesterday...what you had for breakfast this morning...what you watched on television last night? It is hard to imagine life without memory because, if we were unable to remember, life would be a series of fragmentary, unconnected events. But what is memory and how does it work? Cognitive psychologists try to answer these questions. This section focuses on the stages of memory, the characteristics and structure of short-term memory (STM) and long-term memory (LTM), and the differences between them.

Item 1
The stages of memory

You can probably remember when you first met your psychology teacher. You would have told the teacher your name and in the next class he or she might have remembered it. But how did your teacher remember your name?

Psychologists describe three stages of cognitive processing:

Encoding → **Storage** → **Retrieval**

Put into memory   **Maintain in memory**   **Recover from memory**

In **stage 1**, when you told your teacher your name he or she transformed the sound of your name and **encoded** the representation into memory. In **stage 2**, your encoded name was **stored** in your teacher's memory until you met in the next class when, in **stage 3**, your teacher **retrieved** your name from memory.

Theories of memory suggest that forgetting is the result of a failure of any one of these three stages. If your teacher did not pay attention when you told him/her your name, it may not have been encoded into memory. Perhaps your teacher had too many new names to learn, resulting in your name not being stored in memory. It is possible that although your name was stored in your teacher's memory, for some reason it could not be retrieved.

Psychologists who study memory try to explain the processes that lie behind these three stages of memory and why these processes sometimes go wrong, leading to memory failure.

Item 2
Short-term memory (STM) and long-term memory (LTM)

Psychologists distinguish between **short-term memory (STM)** and **long-term memory (LTM)**. STM cannot hold much information and has limited capacity, whereas LTM can hold an apparently unlimited amount of information and has a vast capacity. George Miller theorised that the capacity of STM is approximately 'seven plus or minus two' pieces of information, but that this capacity can be extended by **chunking**, or combining, small pieces of information. For instance, consider this set of 11 numbers: 0 1 7 2 2 5 9 9 2 3 4. This would exceed the proposed capacity of STM, but if chunked into three parts, i.e. 01722 599 234, it makes a more easily remembered telephone number.

Jacobs (1987): a study of capacity in STM

Aim To research the capacity of STM.

Procedures Participants were presented with strings of letters or digits and were asked to repeat them back in the same order. The length of the string was increased, from three to four, five, six etc., until the participant was unable to repeat the sequence accurately.

Findings On average, participants recalled nine digits and seven letters. The average recall increased with age.

Conclusions STM has a limited storage capacity of between five and nine items, but learned memory techniques (e.g. chunking) may increase capacity as people get older. Since there are 26 letters in the alphabet but only ten digits (0–9), letters may be harder to recall.

Criticisms The research is artificial. In real-life settings people do not usually need to remember strings of meaningless numbers or letters, and the research therefore has low ecological validity. If the information to be remembered has more meaning, it might be remembered better.

Another difference between STM and LTM is that information in STM does not last very long — STM has short duration, possibly less than 30 seconds, whereas information in LTM has long duration and may last a lifetime.

Bahrick et al. (1975): very long-term memories — a study of duration in LTM

Aim To study very long-term memories in a real-life setting.

Procedures There were three tasks:
1 In a free recall test, 392 people were asked to list the names of their ex-classmates.
2 In a photo recognition task, participants were shown photographs of their ex-classmates and asked if they could remember the names.
3 In a name recognition task, participants were given names of their ex-classmates and asked to find the matching photographs.

Findings Within 15 years of leaving school, participants were 60% accurate in the free recall task and could recognise 90% of the faces and names. Within 48 years of leaving school, participants were 30% accurate in the free recall task and could recognise 75% of the faces and names. Free recall memory had declined more than photo and name recognition memory.

Conclusions The study shows evidence of very long-term memories in a real-life setting. Since recognition was more accurate than free recall, there may be information stored in memory that can only be accessed when we are given an appropriate cue.

Criticisms This study was undertaken in a real-life setting and the memories were meaningful to the participants, so it has high ecological validity. It is also a useful study as it has application in real life. For example, carers could show elderly people photographs of their colleagues in arms in the Second World War in order to engage them in conversation. In real-life settings, however, variables are hard to control (such as how long a participant had attended the school), leading to less reliability than in laboratory studies.

Recency and primacy effects in STM and LTM

You may have discovered that when you revise for exams you tend to remember information you have learned most recently. This is called the **recency effect**. Glanzer and Cunitz (1966) researched the recency effect in free recall experiments in which people who were asked to memorise lists of words were then asked to recall the words in any order. Usually, the last few words on the list were remembered more frequently, possibly because they could be retrieved from STM. Glanzer and Cunitz also found a **primacy effect**, in that the earliest words were also remembered more frequently, possibly because they had been rehearsed more and had been transferred to LTM. Perhaps when teachers have long lists of names to remember they are more likely to remember the first and last few names they hear.

Item 3
Encoding information in STM and LTM

When we **encode** information in memory we store it in a way that ensures it will be remembered. Sometimes information is encoded **acoustically** (what the information sounds like), sometimes **iconically** (what the information looks like) and sometimes **semantically** (what the information means).

Psychologists suggest differences in the ways in which information is encoded in STM and LTM. In STM, it is often the sound of the information that is encoded, resulting in acoustic code. If you look up a telephone number, you may repeat the number again and again; in effect you rehearse the sound to enable acoustic encoding in STM. In LTM, however, it is the meaning of information that is encoded, resulting in **semantic** code.

Baddeley (1966): investigating encoding in STM and LTM

Aim To look at the effects of acoustic and semantic encoding on recall from STM and LTM.

Procedures Participants were given four sets of words from the following groups:
- acoustically similar (e.g. ban, bad, bat)
- acoustically dissimilar (e.g. sad, pit, bet)
- semantically similar (e.g. big, huge, large)
- semantically dissimilar (e.g. sad, hot, cow)

They were asked to recall as many words as possible, either immediately or after 20 minutes.

Findings In the immediate recall situation (recall supposed to be from STM), participants had more difficulty remembering the acoustically similar words.

In the delayed recall condition (recall supposed to be from LTM), participants had more difficulty remembering the semantically similar words.

Conclusions The difference in the difficulty suggests that STM relies on acoustic encoding while LTM relies on semantic encoding.

Criticisms The research is artificial. In real-life settings people do not usually need to remember strings of short words, and the research therefore has low ecological validity. Miller and Jacobs both agree that if information can be 'chunked' into meaningful segments, it may be remembered better. Also, in addition to **semantic memory**, where the meaning of information is remembered, psychologists have proposed several other ways in which long-term memory can be categorised, which this study does not consider. These include:

- **episodic memory** — memory of specific events, for instance last Christmas or a special occasion
- **procedural memory** — memory of knowing how to do things, such as how to swim or ride a bicycle
- **declarative memory** — where we store learned facts, such as knowing that Paris is the capital city of France

Positron emission tomography (PET) scans of brain activity have found that different areas of the brain may be involved when different types of memories are retrieved.

Summary: STM and LTM

Memory is complex. In order to learn, we must encode, store and be able to retrieve information from memory. The table below shows some of the ways in which STM and LTM are different.

Comparison	Short-term memory (STM)	Long-term memory (LTM)
Capacity	Limited (7 +/− 2 chunks)	Potentially unlimited
Duration	Short (seconds only)	Possibly lifelong
Encoding	Acoustic (sound)	Semantic (meaning) Episodic (events) Procedural (knowing how) Declarative (knowing that)
Order effect	Recency Last information recalled	Primacy First information recalled

1 Read Items 1, 2 and 3 and then complete the crossword on STM and LTM. It should take you about 10 minutes.

Across

3 The process by which information in STM can be retained for longer. (9)

5 Memories of childhood can be stored in this part of your memory (begins with 'L'). (4-4, 6)

7 This is limited in STM and begins with 'C'. (8)

8 This type of memory concerns 'knowing that…', e.g. 'I know that Christmas Day is on 25 December'. (11)

12 The first process by which a memory is stored. (8)

13 The process by which we recover stored memories. (9)

14 This type of memory is for specific events and begins with 'E'. (8)

15 How the capacity of STM can be increased. (8)

Down

1 These effects might be demonstrated when people try to remember lists of words. (7 & 7 — *do* include the ampersand)

2 This type of memory concerns how we remember how to do something, e.g. 'I know how to drive a car'. (10)

4 Where information might be stored initially (or sensory memory). (5-4, 6)

6 The person who proposed the capacity of STM to be 'seven plus or minus two'. (6, 6)

9 This type of encoding takes place when information is stored according to its sound. (8)

10 A word beginning with 'D' meaning how long memories last. (8)

11 This type of encoding takes place when information is stored according to its meaning. (8)

Topic 1: Short-term memory and long-term memory

2 Read Items 2, 3 and 4. Use all 12 words in the list below to fill in the blanks in the story:

- chunked
- Miller
- 30 seconds
- remember
- capacity
- capacity
- rehearsed
- short-term memory
- repeated
- duration
- chunked
- acoustic

2 Daphne ran to answer her phone but as she picked it up it stopped ringing. She dialled 1471 and listened to the recorded voice telling her that the call came from number 016367456899. Not recognising the number, Daphne .... the number over and over again so that it would be retained in her .... As she .... the string of numbers she .... them into three sections as 01636 745 6899. George .... proposes that the .... of STM is 7 plus or minus 2 digits. If this is correct, unless the 12-digit telephone number is .... into smaller units it will exceed the .... of Daphne's STM. Since Daphne did not write down the number she had to use a process of .... encoding to store it in STM. However, just as Daphne began to dial the number her postman arrived and two letters dropped through her letterbox. She picked them up and put them on the hall table. Oh no! Now she could not .... the telephone number. Perhaps that was because the .... of information in STM is less than ....

3 Read Items 2, 3 and 4 and the relevant sections of your textbook and complete sentences **a**, **b** and **c**.

3a When we **encode** information in memory we ....

b When we discuss the **capacity** of memory we are talking about ....

c Information in short-term memory has a short **duration**, which means that ....

4 Read Items 1, 2 and 3. Describe *two* ways in which STM differs from LTM.

4

5 Read Item 2. Outline the aims, procedures and findings of any *one* study of capacity in STM.

5

6 Read Item 3. Outline the findings and conclusions of any *one* study of the duration of memories in LTM.

6

7 Read your textbook and Items 1, 2 and 3. Using the table, summarise the aims, procedures, findings, conclusions and criticisms of *two* research studies into the capacity and duration of STM and LTM.

	Study 1: researcher(s)	Study 2: researcher(s)
Aim (AO1 skill)		
Procedures (AO1 skill)		
Findings (AO1 skill)		
Conclusions (AO1 skill)		
Criticisms (AO2 skill)		

Topic 2 Models of memory

In this topic you will learn about models of memory: the **multi-store model**, the **working memory model** and/or the **levels of processing theory**. You must be able to describe two models, be aware of their strengths and limitations and be familiar with appropriate research evidence.

As you know, research suggests that there are two distinctive memory stores, STM and LTM. You may wish that all the psychology you have ever been taught could be reliably transferred to your LTM. Models, or theories, of memory aim to explain how information is transferred from STM to LTM, and why sometimes it is not.

Item 1
The Atkinson and Shiffrin (1968) multi-store model of memory

In their multi-store model of memory, Atkinson and Shiffrin suggest that memory comprises three separate stores: the **sensory memory store**, the **STM** and the **LTM**. Each store has a specific function:

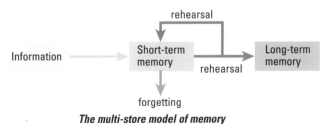

The multi-store model of memory

The diagram shows information being rehearsed in STM and, if rehearsed enough, being transferred to LTM.

There are three stages of information processing in the multi-store model of memory.
- **Stage 1** — information is perceived (seen, heard etc.).
- **Stage 2** — the information is transferred to STM, where it is maintained by rehearsal (if not lost or replaced by new, incoming information).
- **Stage 3** — the information is transferred to LTM.

One strength of the multi-store model is its simplicity. Another is that research evidence supports the idea that STM and LTM are qualitatively different types of memory. Also, we have all, from time to time, 'rehearsed' information and it seems to make sense that rehearsed information is more likely to be remembered. Real-life memories, however, are created in contexts rather different from laboratory-based 'free recall' experiments, so perhaps this model, which is easy to test, does not explain fully the complexities of human memory.

Item 2
The Baddeley and Hitch (1974) model of working memory

The Baddeley and Hitch model of working memory is more complex than the Atkinson and Shiffrin model but it focuses solely on STM or, as Baddeley and Hitch call it, working memory. They propose a multi-store model of STM. In their model, STM is an active processor in which the central executive 'attends to and works on' *either* speech-based information passed to it from the articulatory–phonological loop *or* visually coded information passed to it by the visual system. The three components of this model are:

- **The central executive**
  The central executive processes information from all sensory routes; this process is 'attention-like', having limited capacity.
- **The articulatory–phonological loop**
  This processes speech-based information. The phonological store focuses on speech perception (incoming speech) and the articulatory process focuses on speech production.
- **The visuo-spatial working area**
  This is where spatial and visual information is processed (also known as the visuo-spatial scratchpad).

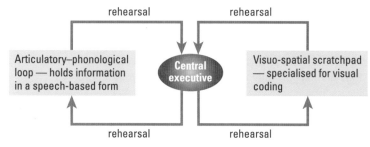

The working memory model

The Baddeley and Hitch working memory model can be tested by the 'interference task' technique. This technique is based on the assumption that the articulatory–phonological loop and the visuo-spatial scratchpad both have limited capacity to process information, so when participants are asked to perform two tasks, using the same system at the same time, their performance is affected. For instance, repeating 'the the the' silently while reading is difficult because both these tasks use the articulatory–phonological loop, which has limited capacity; it cannot cope with both tasks, so the performance of one or the other will be affected.

A strength of the Baddeley and Hitch working memory model is that it suggests rehearsal as an optional process, which is more realistic than the Atkinson and Shiffrin model. (The Atkinson and Shiffrin model suggests that rehearsal is the single cognitive activity involved in transferring information from STM to LTM.) A weakness of the working memory model is that least is known about the precise function of the most important component, the central executive. It may be that the idea of a single central executive is inaccurate.

Item 3
The Craik and Lockhart (1972) levels of processing theory

Craik and Lockhart emphasise the cognitive processes, rather than the structure, of memory. They theorise that whether or not we remember information depends on how it is processed. They describe three levels of processing:

- **iconic** — what information looks like (e.g. daughter)
- **acoustic** — what information sounds like ('doorter')
- **semantic** — what information means (female offspring)

In terms of levels of processing, iconic processing is shallow, acoustic processing is deeper and semantic processing is the deepest. Information that is processed deeply will be remembered better than shallowly processed information.

A strength of the levels of processing theory is that it seems obvious that if we think about information for a long time we are more likely to remember it. However, the theory does not explain fully the different cognitive processes that may be involved in the three levels of processing.

Item 4

Once upon a time everyone (well, almost everyone) knew that if they needed to phone someone but did not have the number, they just dialled 192 for directory enquiries. Then the 192 service was discontinued. All was not lost, however, as many companies began to advertise their directory services in advance of the changeover. Every day for weeks, radio and television advertisements told people the new numbers they could ring. Throughout the UK, in towns and cities, large posters advertised the new directory numbers. In spite of all this effort, however, many people admit they do not know what number to ring if they need a directory service.

Item 5

List A

bean	blue	pink	carrot
cow	diamond	gold	green
horse	kitten	mouse	onion
opal	pea	pearl	potato
puppy	purple	red	silver

List B

potato	kitten	blue	diamond
onion	horse	purple	pearl
carrot	cow	pink	opal
bean	mouse	green	gold
pea	puppy	red	silver

Item 6

St Learnalot, a small primary school, is holding its annual sponsored spelling competition. Marie, a trainee teacher, has promised to help the children learn as many spellings as possible. She takes the list of spellings home and reads through them. There seem an awful lot of words for the children to learn.

St Learnalot: Year 5 sponsored spell (60 words)

table	bathroom	could	kitchen	purple	snow
agree	better	crying	knife	queen	table
about	bicycle	dreaming	laughing	quiet	taller
almost	bigger	eight	mauve	quite	television
addition	black	fright	might	reading	white
aeroplane	blue	garage	orange	running	window
astronaut	brown	green	ought	should	wishing
break	carpet	happiness	paint	shouting	would
behave	chair	house	pink	skipping	writing
before	cooker	jumping	present	smile	yellow

Topic 2: Models of memory

Answers

1 Read Item 1.

  a Describe the Atkinson and Shiffrin multi-store model of memory.

1a

  b Outline why the multi-store model of memory suggests that primary/recency effects will occur when we try to remember lists of words.

b

  c Describe *one* weakness of the multi-store model of memory.

c

2 Read Item 2.

a Draw a labelled diagram of the Baddeley and Hitch working memory model.

2a

b Briefly describe the working memory model.

b

c Give *two* criticisms of this model. (**Hint:** criticisms can be positive and/or negative.)

c

3 Read Item 3. Outline the three levels of processing proposed by Craik and Lockhart.

3

4 Read Item 4, which concludes that 'many people admit they do not know what number to ring if they need a directory service'. Explain why people have not remembered one of the advertised numbers, with reference to:
a the multi-store model of memory
b the working memory model
c the levels of processing model

4a

b

c

5 Use Items 3 and 5 to conduct a small experiment. Show five of your friends the 20 words organised in Item 5: List A, and ask them to try to remember them. Show a different group of five friends the 20 words in List B and ask them to try to remember them. (Let both groups look at the lists of words for about 2 minutes.) Then ask them to write down as many of the words as they can remember.
(**Note:** each list contains the same words.)

a The levels of processing theory predicts that people who are shown List B will remember more words than those shown List A. Referring to your findings and to this theory, explain why this might happen.

b Outline *two* criticisms of the Craik and Lockhart levels of processing model.

c Briefly describe psychological evidence that supports the levels of processing theory of memory. (**Note:** you will need to refer to your textbook to do some research.)

5a

b

c

Topic 2: Models of memory

6 Read Item 6. Referring to any *two* of the models of memory, complete the chart to suggest how Marie can help the pupils at St Learnalot do well in their sponsored spelling competition.

(**Hint:** for each of the two models, you might structure your answer as follows: Which model of memory are you using? What could the pupils do? Why, according to the model, should they do this? What might be the result?)

6	**Model:**	**Model:**
	Pupil action:	Pupil action:
	Why?	Why?
	Predicted result?	Predicted result?

7 *Exam preparation*
Referring to your textbook and to the items in this topic, make brief notes on *two* models of memory.

Model of memory		
Outline: proposed cognitive structures/ processes		
Research (evidence) in support of the model (AO1 skill)		
Strength(s) of the model and/or evidence (AO2 skill)		
Weakness(es) of the model and/or evidence (AO2 skill)		
Possible application in real life? (AO2 skill)		

Topic 3 Forgetting

Forgetting is when we are unable to retrieve a memory, or when we never had a memory in the first place — we may forget because we did not store the information in LTM.

This topic covers explanations for forgetting in STM (decay and displacement) and LTM (retrieval failure and interference), as well as emotional factors in remembering and forgetting, including psychodynamic (Freudian) explanations for forgetting (repression of unpleasant memories) and flashbulb memories.

Item 1
Forgetting in STM

If you don't pay attention in lessons, you will probably not be able to remember what you are taught. This does not mean that the information has been forgotten, but simply that it was never learned. You might say that you forgot it, but learning only applies to LTM. You won't learn anything if the information is only held in STM for a few seconds.

Trace decay theory in STM is based on the idea that information in STM will only be retained for a short duration; it claims that STM cannot hold information for more than 30 seconds unless it is rehearsed. The **Brown-Petersen 'trigram technique'** tested the theory of trace decay. In simple terms, according to trace decay theory, information in STM is forgotten, unless rehearsed, because the memory fades away.

In simple terms, according to **displacement theory**, information in STM (which has limited capacity) is forgotten because it

is pushed out (displaced) by new information. **Waugh and Norman (1965)** designed the **serial probe experiment** to test this theory.

Item 2
Forgetting in LTM

Several factors are thought to cause forgetting in LTM:

Interference This theory proposes that what we have already learned can affect whether we remember new information (**proactive interference**). It also claims that when we learn new information it may affect whether we can remember previous learning (**retroactive interference**).

Retrieval failure Some psychologists propose that when we are unable to recall information from LTM this is not because learning has been forgotten, but rather because we have not used an appropriate **cue**.

Context dependency Some psychologists propose that in order to facilitate memory we need to be in the same context as when we learned the information, for example in the same physical surroundings, with the same people. Abernethy (1940) investigated the effect of context on recall.

State dependency Another theory proposes that to remember most effectively we need to be in the same emotional state as we were when learning took place. **Tulving and Psotka (1971)** investigated cue-dependent forgetting.

Item 3
Two studies of forgetting in LTM

Tulving and Psotka (1971): cue-dependent forgetting

Aim To test the theory of interference and cue-dependent forgetting.

Procedures Participants were given multiple lists of 24 words to remember. Each list was presented as six categories of four words. In the **free recall** condition, participants were asked to remember as many of the words as they could. In the **cued recall** condition, participants were told the category names (the cues) and asked to remember the words.

Findings In the free recall condition, there was evidence of retroactive interference. Participants who had fewer lists remembered more words than those who had more lists. This suggests that learning the later lists interfered with what had been learned from the earlier lists. In the cued recall condition, there was no effect of retroactive interference. Participants remembered about 70% of the words from each list.

Conclusions Interference does not always cause forgetting. Memories were available when a cue was used. Forgetting in the free recall condition was cue-dependent. This may mean that memory in LTM is accessible if we use an appropriate cue.

Abernethy (1940): an experimental study of the effect of external context on recall

Procedures Psychology students were tested before they began a 4 week course. During the course, all of the students had the same lecturer and the sessions took place in the same room. At the end of each week, the students were tested in one of four conditions:
- same room with usual lecturer
- same room with different lecturer
- different room with usual lecturer
- different room with different lecturer

Findings The students who were tested in the same room by their usual lecturer achieved the best results.

Conclusions The context (the room and the lecturer) had in some way provided cues to memory. Perhaps when the students gazed around while they tried to remember they noticed something that acted as a cue to their memory.

Criticisms This was a field experiment and therefore control of the variables other than the context would have been difficult. Perhaps some students were more motivated and revised harder. This lack of control over variables may have led to low validity and reliability. However, this was a real-life study and the results of the tests mattered to the students, so ecological validity was high.

Item 4
Asif is in a muddle

Asif was in his bedroom revising for his psychology exam. In the morning he made notes on the multi-store model of memory. After lunch he read his textbook and made notes on the working memory model. When Sophie, one of his friends, popped in for a chat, she agreed to test him on what he had learned. While Sophie tested Asif, they sat in the kitchen and had a coffee. But oh dear, poor Asif! He found he was getting his models of memory in a dreadful muddle.

Item 5
Emotion and memory

Emotion affects our memories in two ways. Highly emotional events may be either more memorable or less memorable than everyday events.

Flashbulb memories can be described as memories of emotional events that last for a lifetime. Many older people remember where they were and what they were doing when they heard that President J. F. Kennedy had been assassinated. You may remember clearly what you were doing when you heard about the events of 11 September 2001. (**Hint:** read your textbook to review the **Brown & Kulik (1977)** research study into flashbulb memory.)

It has been suggested that flashbulb memories are **photographic** and **long-lasting**. The idea of flashbulb memory appears to contradict the theory that information has to be processed in STM before a long-term memory is created. Flashbulb memory seems to suggest that how we feel about our information (our emotions) is important.

Conway et al. (1994): Mrs Thatcher resigns! A study of flashbulb memory

Aim To show that events that have distinctive meaning for people are likely to be remembered clearly.

Procedures A group of 923 participants, two-thirds UK residents and one-third non-UK residents (mainly American), were tested 2 weeks after Margaret Thatcher's resignation. Three hundred and sixty-nine of them were tested again 11 months later. All were asked a series of questions to assess how clear their memories of the event were.

Findings Of the UK nationals, 86% had a flashbulb memory of the event whereas only 29% of the non-UK nationals had a flashbulb memory. In addition, the memories of the UK nationals were more detailed and were consistent over time.

Conclusions Events that have cultural significance are more likely to be remembered clearly by people to whom the events are significant than they are by people to whom they are not so significant.

Application If this is the case, then New Yorkers are more likely to remember clearly the events of 11 September 2001 than other Americans, who in turn are more likely than non-Americans to remember clearly the events of that day.

Criticisms It is difficult to be certain that what people tell us about their memories is accurate. If a person says that he or she 'watched the event at Uncle Joe's house while eating a fish-and-chip supper' this may or may not be true, even if the participant believes it to be the case! Also, since surprising or shocking events become topics for discussion, one person's memory can be influenced by hearing other people discussing their memories of the event.

Item 6
Repressed memories (unconscious motivation for forgetting)

Freud suggested that **repression** is the way we protect our ego (conscious mind) from unpleasant memories. Traumatic memories are repressed from consciousness and are therefore unavailable. Unhappy or traumatic memories are more likely to be forgotten than happy memories: we are unconsciously **motivated to forget** information, or events, that make us uncomfortable.

Levinger and Clarke (1961) devised a free association experiment to test the theory and found that participants took longer to respond to emotional words, such as quarrel, angry and fear, than to neutral words, such as window, cow and tree. They also measured GSR (galvanic skin response — a measure of emotional arousal) and found higher measures of arousal for the emotional words. After the word association tests, they used the same word cues again and asked participants to remember their initial responses. They reported that participants had difficulty remembering their responses to the emotional words.

On the other hand, **Christianson and Hubinette (1993)** found that emotional involvement increases the accuracy of memory. They interviewed 110 people who had witnessed a bank robbery. Those witnesses who had been personally threatened during the crime, and who must have been more emotionally involved, had more accurate memories than the witnesses who said they were not very involved.

Repressed memories: criticisms

The major challenge to the theory of repressed memory is how to test it in a way that results in valid findings and conclusions. Since, according to Freud, repressed memories reside in the unconscious, how can we test whether they are accurate when they 'surface'? In cases where recovered memories lead to parents/relatives being accused of child abuse, the reliability of the recovered memory is critically important, but can this memory ever be verified? Unlike flashbulb memories for public events (which can sometimes be verified against records), repressed memories are private and family members may all have their own individual memories. Studies that measure responses to 'threatening words' may not be a valid measure, as they may be measuring the emotive responses to the words, rather than any repressed memory.

Item 7
Motivated forgetting

Susan is a staff nurse in a breast cancer clinic. Every day she counsels women who have just been told that they need surgery to remove a potentially cancerous lump from their breast. It is Susan's responsibility to ensure that patients are given the information they need and that they understand what is going to happen when they are admitted for their operation. At the close of the counselling session, patients are given an information leaflet and are told they can ring Susan's helpline if they have any worries.

Regardless of how much time she spends with each patient, and how well they seem to have understood, Susan spends a long time on the phone to patients re-explaining what they have already been told.

1 Read Item 1.

a Define the terms 'memory' and 'forgetting'.

b Describe *two* factors that influence forgetting in STM.

c Explain whether or not theories of forgetting in STM reflect real life.

2 Read Items 2 and 3.

a Write definitions of the following terms:
  (i) proactive interference
  (ii) retroactive interference
  (iii) cue-dependent forgetting

1a

b

c

2a

b Outline the findings and conclusions of *two* studies of forgetting in LTM. (**Hint:** you do not need to learn studies of forgetting in LTM in detail but you do need to know a range of findings/conclusions/criticisms. In the exam, you could be asked: 'Describe the *findings* of research into forgetting in LTM' or 'Describe the *conclusions* of research into forgetting in LTM'.)

b

c Outline the strengths and weaknesses of *one* of the studies you described in part **b**.

c

3 Use all the words listed below to complete the blanks in this review of why we may forget.

- forgotten
- displaced
- trace
- sounds
- iconic
- decay
- interferes
- three
- multi-store
- new
- cue
- rehearsed
- semantic
- remember
- semantics
- retroactive
- order
- process

4 Read Item 5.
Explain what is meant by a 'flashbulb memory'.

3 In short-term memory, information may be .... because it is .... by new information. Or perhaps the .... of the information may .... because it is not .... The Atkinson and Shiffrin .... model suggests that the amount of information and the .... in which information is received may predict whether we .... it. The Craik and Lockhart model of memory suggests that the way we .... information is important. This model proposes .... levels of processing: ...., which is a shallow level of processing in which we focus on what information looks like; acoustic, in which we focus on what information .... like; and ...., which is the deepest level of processing. If we think about the meaning of the information, the ...., we are less likely to forget it. Psychologists have also suggested that we forget information held in LTM because .... learning .... with existing learning (this is .... interference). Sometimes we cannot remember information unless we have a meaningful ...., which is called cue-dependent forgetting.

4

5 Read Item 4. Based on psychological research, make *two* suggestions as to why Asif has muddled his memory models, and what would help Asif (and Sophie to help him) revise more effectively.

5

6 Refer to Item 5 and to your textbook and answer the following questions about the Conway (1994) study of flashbulb memory.

6a

a What were the aims of the study?

b Describe the procedures.

b

c Outline the findings of the study.

c

d What conclusions did Conway reach and is the research useful in real life? (Why or why not?)

d

e Describe why the findings of research into flashbulb memories may not be reliable.

e

7 Read Item 6.

a Complete the crossword.

Across

3&5 How Levinger and Clarke tested the theory of repressed memory. (4,11)

7 He proposed the theory of repressed memories. (5)

9 The part of the mind in which repressed memories may be stored — begins with 'U'. (11)

11 Fear, happiness, shock or joy are examples of this — begins with 'E'. (7)

12 Add 'psycho' to a word beginning with 'D' that means 'active' or 'potent' and you get the psychological approach that explains repressed memories. (13)

Down

1 A measure of emotional arousal. (3)

2 The kind of memory we may forget — begins with 'U'. (10)

4 Push into the unconscious mind. (7)

6 This type of memory may be repressed. (9)

8 Part of the conscious mind. (3)

10 What you are studying — begins with 'M'. (6)

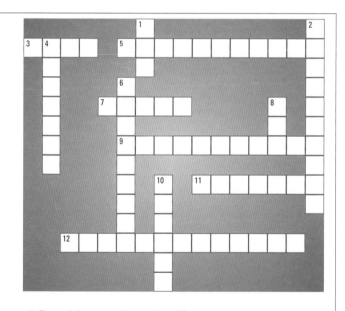

b Describe the procedures, findings and conclusions of *one* study of repressed memories.

b

8 Read Item 7. Apply what you have learned about forgetting and about repressed memories.

a Explain to Susan why her patients may forget much of the information they have been given.

b What could Susan do to increase the probability of her patients being able to remember the information they have been given?

8a

b

9 *Exam practice*

Review the items on forgetting in STM and LTM. To what extent do emotional factors influence memory and/or forgetting?

- Write a list of points as an outline plan for this essay. In your outline, identify the psychological evidence you will use and the evaluative points you will make.
- In a full exam you would, in about 100 words, describe appropriate psychological evidence (AO1 skills), and then provide about 200 words of evaluative commentary (AO2 skills).

An eyewitness is someone present at an event such as a crime or an accident. But how reliable is the memory of what he or she has witnessed? This is a real-world question to which we can apply the findings and conclusions of psychological research.

Item 1
Research into eyewitness testimony: Loftus and Palmer (1974)

Loftus and Palmer conducted research into the accuracy of eyewitness testimony. In Experiment 1 they investigated the effect of **leading questions** on eyewitness accounts, and in Experiment 2 they investigated the effects that leading questions have on later memory of what happened. The leading question they asked was, 'How fast were the cars going when they smashed into each other?' This is a leading question because the verb 'smashed' suggests that the cars were travelling fast. The verb 'bumped' would suggest a slower speed.

Experiment 1
Forty-five student participants viewed a short video of a car accident. The participants were divided into five groups of nine students. After watching the video, each group was given a questionnaire that included the leading question. However, a slightly different version of the critical question was given to each group in that the verb varied: it was either 'smashed', 'collided', 'bumped', 'hit' or 'contacted'. As shown in the bar chart, the leading question affected the participants' perception

of speed. The conclusion was that the way questions are worded may affect perception and recall.

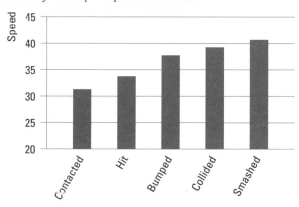

Experiment 1: estimated speed for verb used

Experiment 2
Loftus and Palmer researched a second question to find out whether leading questions affect the way the information is stored in memory and later retrieved.

One hundred and fifty student participants (three groups of 50) viewed a short video of a car accident. Afterwards they were given a questionnaire. The critical leading question was, 'How fast were the cars going when they smashed into each other?'

Group 1 was asked the critical question containing the word 'hit', group 2 was asked it with the word 'smashed' and group 3 (the control group) was not asked the critical/leading question. A week later, the participants were asked to return and answer more questions, including 'Did you see any broken glass?' (there was no broken glass in the film clip). The findings are shown in the bar chart. Those participants who thought the car was travelling faster (the 'smashed' group) were more likely to report seeing broken glass. This suggests that their memory of a car travelling faster led them to 'invent' a memory in line with this expectation. The findings from these two experiments suggest that leading questions do have an effect on what eyewitnesses think they have seen.

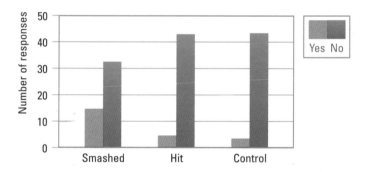

Response to 'Did you see any broken glass?'

Item 2
Leading questions: Loftus and Zanni (1975)

Loftus and Zanni (1975) showed a short film of a car accident. One group of 'witnesses' were asked if they had seen '*the*' broken headlight. A second group of witnesses were asked if they had seen '*a*' broken headlight. Out of those who had been asked about '*the*' headlight, 17% reported seeing it, compared with 7% of those who had been asked about '*a*' headlight. This shows that even apparently trivial words can affect a memory of an event.

Item 3
Reconstructive memory: filling in the gaps

Schema are mental structures that hold ready-made opinions, beliefs and expectations about the world. The way information is encoded into memory can be affected by existing schema (e.g. cars that 'smashed' were travelling fast). Existing schema can affect the way information is learned (remembered) and how it is recalled (reconstructed).

Frederick Bartlett (1932) theorised that memory is an **active process**. He claimed that we only store some elements of new experiences in memory, and when we remember the events we reconstruct them, filling in missing information with information from learned schema, such as stored opinions, prejudices, expectations or stereotypes. In his **'War of the Ghosts'** story, he showed that people change unfamiliar information to fit their individual cultural schema.

Bartlett proposed that we remember the meaning of information, and that gaps are filled in by familiar information in order to make the story/event more meaningful and thus easier to remember.

Item 4
Bartlett (1932): 'War of the Ghosts' (a synopsis)

Participants were asked to read a short story from a different culture containing unfamiliar words. After a few days, they were asked to recall the story. The recalled stories were always shorter than the original versions. The unfamiliar parts and words were changed to fit in with the readers' culture (e.g. canoe was changed to boat). The recalled version became fixed over time as the version that was remembered. Bartlett concluded that it is the meaning of a story that we remember, and that unfamiliar material is skewed towards a culturally biased interpretation. However, later studies have found that if participants are told that accurate recall is required, there are fewer changes when the story is remembered.

Item 5
Cohen (1981): do stereotypes influence how we remember?

Aim To find out whether being told that a person is a waitress or a librarian will influence how that person is remembered.

Procedures Participants were shown a 15-minute video of a man and a woman having a meal to celebrate a birthday. There were four conditions:

- **Waitress before:** before the film was shown, participants were told that the woman was a waitress.
- **Waitress after:** after the film was shown, participants were told that the woman was a waitress.
- **Librarian before:** before the film was shown, participants were told that the woman was a librarian.
- **Librarian after:** after the film was shown, participants were told that the woman was a librarian.

Findings Participants were more likely to recall information that was *consistent* with the stereotype of a waitress or a librarian than information that was inconsistent with it. Participants who received the information *before* the film recalled more accurate information than those who were given the waitress or librarian information afterwards.

Conclusions Cohen concluded that when the information was given before the film it had generated expectations, and that this increased the accuracy of memories.

Criticisms Although a laboratory experiment, this is a realistic situation and shows that how people are described to us may affect the way we form memories of them. The control over the independent variables allowed Cohen to make clear statements about cause and effect. However, making judgements about the personality of strangers after watching a short film is not something that we do every day. The study could thus be said to have good experimental validity but perhaps less ecological validity. A strength is that this study can be replicated to test reliability.

Item 6
Improving the reliability of eyewitness testimony

Geiselman (1985): the cognitive interview

The cognitive interview is a procedure used by the police to help eyewitnesses recall information more accurately. During the interview the witness is encouraged to:

- report every detail, no matter how seemingly trivial
- recreate the context of the event
- recall the event in different orders (in reverse, partially etc.)
- recall the event from other perspectives (imagining what someone in a different place may have seen)

While the interview is progressing, the police take care to:

- reduce the anxiety felt by witnesses
- minimise any distractions
- allow the witness to take his/her time
- avoid interruptions and leading questions

This type of interview has been found to achieve up to 35% improvement in the accuracy of recall, especially if the interview takes place shortly after the event.

Item 7
Eyewitness: a ruined evening

Adam and Eve were shocked. They had been on their way to the cinema and as they walked from the car park they had been chatting about their forthcoming exams. They had both been revising all day and were looking forward to a relaxed evening. As they reached the entrance to the car park, two masked men ran from a nearby street, followed by a man with blood running down his face, who was shouting for help. A van screeched round the corner and halted briefly while the running men jumped in. As it roared off, the van sideswiped a parked car. Seconds later, with sirens screaming and lights flashing, two police cars arrived and five police officers jumped out. Apparently there had been an armed robbery. Since Adam and Eve had seen the men and the van, they were asked to go to the police station to make a statement. In lengthy interviews they were each asked to describe the men and the van. Their evening was ruined!

1 Read Item 1. Complete the crossword (some clues refer to previous topics).

Across

1&2 Long-lasting memories of shocking events. (9, 8)

5 When we can't remember, we…. (6)

7 Freud suggested we are motivated to forget traumatic events (this process begins with 'R'). (10)

10 Someone who *hears* an event 'first hand'. (10)

12 'War of the Ghosts' was a story used in whose research? (0)

13&14 Questions that suggest a certain answer. (7, 9)

15 Which two researchers studied eyewitness testimony? (6 & 6 …and *do* include the ampersand)

Down

2 The hypothetical 'place' in which learning is stored. (6)

3 This word refers to meaning (begins with 'S'). (8)

4 Rebuilding a memory from schema and cues. (14)

6 This hormone may lead to traumatic memories lasting a lifetime (begins with 'A'). (10)

8 Someone who observes an event 'first hand'. (10)

9 The basic meaning of a story (begins with 'G'). (4)

11 Mental structures that organise information and experience. (6)

2 Read Item 1 and your textbook.

a Explain what is meant by eyewitness testimony.

b Explain what a leading question is.

c State whether the following are leading questions and, if so, why.
(i) Have you seen the cat?
(ii) Have you seen a cat?
(iii) Was the tall woman wearing a black hat or a red hat?
(iv) Did you see the weapon?
(v) Who had the weapon, the man in the garage or the man by the car?

d Describe the procedures and findings of *one* study of eyewitness testimony.

2a

b

c

d

Topic 4: Critical issue: eyewitness testimony

e What conclusions did the researchers of the study you described in part **d** draw as to how leading questions may affect the memories of eyewitnesses?

f Describe *one* strength and *one* weakness of either the Loftus and Palmer research (see Item 1) or the Loftus and Zanni research (see Item 2).

(**Hint:** remember to explain why the strength you describe is a strength and why the weakness is a weakness.)

e

f

3 Read Item 4. Here is a version with the words scrambled. Without referring to the original, put the words in each sentence in the correct order so that it reads like the original version. Then compare your version with the original.

3 **Bartlett (1932): 'War of the Ghosts' (a synopsis)**

Participants were read asked to a short from culture story a containing different unfamiliar words.

After a story days they few were asked to recall the.

The were recalled versions shorter than stories always the original.

The parts and words were unfamiliar e.g. fit changed boat to in with the readers' (canoe was changed to culture).

The version became fixed over recalled time as the remembered version that was.

Bartlett meaning concluded that it is the of a remember story that we, and that skewed unfamiliar is towards a biased material culturally interpretation.

However, studies have found later that if told participants are that required changes accurate remembered recall is there is fewer when the story are.

4 Read about reconstructive memory in your textbook and Items 3, 4 and 5.
  a In your own words, explain what psychologists mean when they refer to schema.
  b In about 60 words, outline Bartlett's theory of reconstructive memory.

4a

b

Topic 4: Critical issue: eyewitness testimony

c Describe *two* processes involved in reconstructive memory.

c

d Describe the aims, procedures and findings of *one* study of reconstructive memory.

d

5 Review your notes on eyewitness testimony and reread the items, particularly Item 7.

a According to Loftus and Palmer, why might the eyewitness testimonies of Adam and Eve be unreliable?

b According to Bartlett, why might the eyewitness testimonies of Adam and Eve be unreliable?

c According to Brown and Kulik, what were Adam and Eve most likely to remember?

d According to Freud, why might Adam and Eve have been unlikely to remember the details of what they saw?

e According to Tulving and Psotka, why might Adam and Eve have remembered more of what they saw if they were interviewed in the car park?

5a

b

c

d

e

f What could the police do to help Adam and Eve remember what they saw? Outline the interview procedure the police could use and explain why this might be effective.

f

6 *Exam practice*

Review all of the topics on memory. 'Eyewitness testimony is unreliable.' To what extent does psychological research support this statement?

- Write one paragraph outlining supporting evidence, one paragraph outlining the strengths of the research and one paragraph outlining the limitations of the research.
- In a full exam you would, in about 100 words, describe appropriate psychological evidence (AO1 skills), and then provide about 200 words of evaluative commentary (AO2 skills).

Paragraph 1: Evidence
Paragraph 2: Strengths of the research
Paragraph 3: Limitations of the research

Developmental psychologists study the changes that occur as people grow from childhood, through adolescence, and into adulthood. This development includes changes in thought processes and social and emotional behaviour. Attachments, which are strong emotional bonds that form as a result of interaction between two people, occur throughout our life span. The possible benefits of infant attachments are:

- Young animals are helpless at birth and behaviour that ensures closeness to a provider of food and protection aids survival.
- Being with mature animals enables young animals to learn the behaviour important for independent survival and reproduction.
- Attachment forms a basis for emotional relationships. The infant learns how to form loving bonds that are the basis for later adult relationships.

The study of attachment in childhood is of interest because the quality of early attachments may have an effect on the quality of emotional relationships in adulthood.

Item 1
What is meant by 'attachment'?

Schaffer (1993) defined attachment as 'a close emotional relationship between two persons characterised by mutual affection and a desire to maintain closeness'.

Maccoby (1980) defined the characteristics of infant–caregiver attachment as:

- wanting to be near each other (seeking proximity)
- a mutual feeling of distress when separated (separation anxiety)
- pleasure on being reunited
- a general orientation (awareness) from the infant towards the primary caregiver, seeking reassurance that the primary caregiver is 'there'

Schaffer's four stages in the development of attachment

1 **Pre-attachment:** in the first 2–3 months babies learn that people are different from inanimate objects but they do not have any preference regarding who looks after them.
2 **Indiscriminate attachment:** from 3 to about 7 months babies learn to recognise different people and smile more at people they know than at strangers, but they still have no strong preference about who looks after them.
3 **Discriminate attachment:** from 7 months, babies are able to form strong emotional bonds with a specific person. An attachment is evidenced by the infant being contented when the person is present, distressed when they leave (separation protest) and pleased and happy when they return. The infant may show nervousness of strangers (stranger anxiety).

4 **Multiple attachments:** from about 9 months, babies can form attachments to more than one person. Though many attachments can develop, some attachments may be stronger than others and may have different functions.

Item 2
Developing attachments: research by Schaffer and Emerson (1964)

In a longitudinal study, Schaffer and Emerson aimed to find out more information about the development of attachment.

Procedures In a longitudinal study, 60 babies were observed in their homes in Glasgow from when they were 4 weeks old to when they were about 18 months. Their families were also interviewed. Attachment was measured by:

- **separation protest** — e.g. when the infant was left in situations such as being alone in his/her room or pram
- **stranger anxiety** — e.g. when the researcher approached the infant and noted when the infant started to show distress

Findings At 8 months, about 50 of the babies had developed more than one attachment. Although the mother was the main carer, about 20 had a stronger attachment to someone else. Evidence for the four stages of attachment was found.

Conclusions Babies form attachments in stages and can develop attachments to more than one person. The **quality of care** is important in the development of attachments; infants develop attachments to sensitive and loving people, and not necessarily their mother.

Item 3
The development of attachments

The following factors influence the development of attachments:

- **The age of the child: Bowlby** proposed that unless attachments have developed by between 1 and 3 years, they will not develop 'normally'.
- **The child's temperament:** some aspects of temperament may be innate and a child's temperament may make it easier or harder for him/her to form attachments, regardless of the quality of care the child receives.

Evolution, ethology, imprinting and quality of care also influence the forming of attachments.

Evolution

Darwin suggested that the enormous variation in the animal and plant world can be explained in terms of the way each individual species 'fits' its environmental niche. The species that fits the best, and has advantageous physical or behavioural characteristics, is most likely to survive and reproduce. These characteristics are called **adaptive** as they enable the individual to be adapted to its environment.

Ethology: the work of Konrad Lorenz

Lorenz was an ethologist who observed the behaviour of birds and demonstrated how imprinting takes place. He separated a clutch of goose eggs so that when some of the young hatched they did not see their mother but saw Lorenz instead. These goslings followed him around as if he was their mother. Imprinting acts like an invisible piece of string, maintaining proximity between a caregiver and the young. Lorenz tested this bond by placing his goslings with their siblings, reared by their natural mother. When he let them all go, 'his' goslings ran to him and the others ran to the goose.

Imprinting

Imprinting is a concept derived from the study of how embryos develop. During the early stages of development, there are times when certain things form, such as the spinal cord and the legs. If development is interrupted during this **critical period**, then it simply does not take place. **Bowlby (1969)** was impressed by the idea that imprinting is an adaptive behaviour and proposed that the same principle be applied to the attachment between human infants and their caregivers.

Is there a critical period for attachment development?

Bowlby (1969) suggested that there is a sensitive period that ends at around 1–3 years, during which infants develop a special attachment to one individual. **Klaus and Kennell (1976)** proposed that immediately after birth there is a period during which skin-to-skin contact facilitates the development of attachments. **Chateau and Wiberg (1977)** found that mothers who had skin-to-skin contact with and immediately suckled their baby engaged in more kissing, embracing and breast-feeding for an average of $2\frac{1}{2}$ months longer than mothers who had only cuddled their baby. Most psychologists, however, agree that it is unlikely that any experience immediately after birth has an irreversible effect on human infants.

Does the quality of care affect attachment?

Ainsworth et al. (1974) proposed that good, secure attachment is promoted by sensitive responsiveness from a caregiver.

Attachment is not due to a caregiver just being with the infant; it is related to the quality of the interactions between the infant and his/her caregiver. In support of this theory, **Isabella et al. (1989)** found that responsiveness in the mother towards a baby of 1 month old correlated with a close relationship between mother and baby at 1 year.

Harlow (1959)

Harlow placed young monkeys with two 'mothers'. One was a wire 'mother' with a feeding bottle attached and the other 'mother' was covered in cloth but had no feeding bottle. The monkeys showed a preference for the cloth-covered mother, especially when they were distressed, which shows that attachment is not about food alone. Harlow also found that, as adults, these monkeys found it difficult to form reproductive relationships and were poor mothers. This shows that the lack of interaction from a caregiver may be the cause of later maladjustment.

Topic 1: The development of attachments

Answers

1 Read Item 1. Put the words in the scrambled sentence in the correct order to reveal Schaffer's (1993) definition of attachment.

1 closeness to a desire emotional between persons two by characterised close affection a and mutual maintain relationship

2 Read Item 1. Based on Schaffer's four stages in the development of attachment, decide whether the following statements are true or false and explain your choices.
a Emily is 3 weeks old; she cries when her mother leaves the room.
b Peter is 4 months old; he recognises his mother and smiles as she approaches.
c Maryanne is 8 months old; she shows no reaction when her mother hands her to a stranger and leaves the room.
d It is Henry's first birthday. He laughs when his sister plays with him, looks anxious when his mother leaves the room and smiles with pleasure when she returns.

2a TRUE / FALSE because

b TRUE / FALSE because

c TRUE / FALSE because

d TRUE / FALSE because

3 Complete the following sentence: Developing an attachment may be an advantage because…

3

4 Use your textbook and read Item 2.

   a Describe briefly the findings and conclusions of the Schaffer and Emerson (1964) Glasgow study.

   b Outline *two* strengths of this research.

   c Outline *two* weaknesses of this research.

5 Use your textbook and read Item 3. Fill in the blanks using the words and phrases listed below.
- temperament of the child
- quality of care
- develop by the age of 3–5
- individual differences
- the age of the child
- sensitive
- innate
- caring
- physical presence

6 Use your textbook and read Items 1 and 2.

   a Explain what is meant by attachment.

4a _____

b _____

c _____

5 The following factors may influence the development of attachments. First, _____ Bowlby proposed that unless attachments _____ they will never develop 'normally'. Second, the _____. Parents need to be _____ and _____ may not be enough. Third, the _____ which may be _____. The child's temperament may make it easier or harder for him/her to form attachments, regardless of the quality of care he/she receives.

6a _____

Topic 1: The development of attachments

b How is separation anxiety related to attachment?

b

c How is stranger anxiety related to attachment?

c

d What is imprinting?

d

e According to Bowlby, how is the concept of imprinting related to the concept of attachment?

e

f Explain what the research by Lorenz and Harlow tells us about attachment.

f

7 Answer the following questions without referring to your notes.
   a Describe *two* factors that influence the development of attachment.

7a

   b Outline the development of attachments in infants.

b

8 Review the items in Topic 1 and complete this crossword on the development of attachments.

Across

2 Studies that take place over a long period of time. (12)

5 This approach suggests that attachments benefit survival. (12)

8 The hypothesis that infants develop one special attachment (read your textbook!) (9)

9 Researchers who suggested that skin-to-skin contact immediately after birth supports the development of attachments. (5&7…and *do* include the ampersand)

12 The names of two researchers who found evidence that attachments develop in four stages. (8&7…and do include the ampersand)

13 The city in which Schaffer and Emerson studied attachment in babies. (7)

Down

1 This may be shown when an infant is separated from the person to whom he or she is attached (begins with 'P'). (7)

3 The immediate bond formed by the young of some species with the first object they see. (10)

4 This researcher suggested that the quality of attachments in infancy will affect later adult relationships. (6)

6 This emotion is shown when the pair who are attached are reunited (begins with 'P'). (8)

7 This emotion may be shown when an infant is separated from the person to whom he or she is attached (begins with 'D'). (8)

10 This researcher studied infant monkeys and their preference for a cloth-covered mother model. (6)

11 Behaviour that is present at birth (nature not nurture). (6)

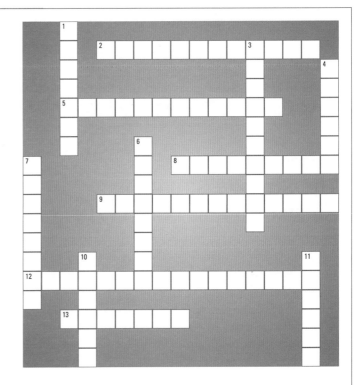

Research has shown that there are individual and cultural differences in styles of attachment. For example, some infants are **securely attached** whereas others are **insecurely attached**. **Ainsworth and Bell (1970)** developed the Strange Situation procedures to measure differences in infant attachment.

Item 1
The Strange Situation: Ainsworth and Bell (1970)

The Strange Situation procedures involve controlled observation that allows researchers to assess how securely an infant is attached to a caregiver. It comprises seven episodes, each lasting about 3 minutes:

1 The caregiver carries the infant into a room and puts the infant on the floor. He/she then sits in a chair and does not interact with the infant unless the infant seeks attention.

2 A stranger enters the room and talks with the caregiver, then approaches the infant with a toy.

3 The caregiver leaves. If the infant plays, the stranger observes unobtrusively. If the infant is passive, the stranger tries to interest him/her in a toy. If the infant shows distress (crying), the stranger tries to comfort him/her.

4 The caregiver returns and the stranger leaves.

5 After the infant has begun to play, the caregiver leaves and the infant is briefly left alone.

6 The stranger re-enters the room and repeats the behaviour as described in step 3.

7 The caregiver returns and the stranger leaves.

This procedure places the infant in a mildly stressful situation in order to observe four behaviours:

- **Separation anxiety:** a securely attached child shows some anxiety but is fairly easily soothed.
- **Willingness to explore:** a securely attached child explores more when the caregiver is present.
- **Stranger anxiety:** the degree of security of attachment is related to the degree of stranger anxiety.
- **Reunion behaviour:** an insecurely attached infant may ignore the caregiver's return.

Behaviours that were characteristic of the whole sample were described as follows:

- **Exploratory behaviour** — three kinds were observed: locomotion, manipulation and visual exploration. All these reduced as soon as the stranger entered.
- **Crying** increased through each stage of the procedure.
- **Proximity-seeking** and contact-maintaining behaviours intensified during the short separations, and were also present in stages 2 and 3 when the stranger appeared.
- **Contact-resisting** and proximity-avoiding behaviours occurred rarely towards the caregiver prior to separation, but in stage 5 about a third of the sample showed such behaviour towards their caregiver and about half of the children showed such behaviour in the last episode.

Item 2
Individual differences in the Strange Situation: Ainsworth et al. (1972)

Ainsworth et al. (1972) distinguished between three attachment types:
- secure
- insecure-avoidant
- insecure-resistant

Secure attachment

Securely attached infants show some anxiety when their caregiver departs but are easily soothed and greet the caregiver's return with enthusiasm. These infants play independently and return to the caregiver regularly for reassurance.

Ainsworth et al. concluded that a secure attachment is associated with sensitivity in the caregiver, which teaches the infant to expect the same in other relationships. Secure attachment is generally related to healthy cognitive and emotional development, involving independence, self-confidence and trusting relationships.

Insecure-avoidant attachment

The infant shows indifference when the caregiver leaves, and does not display stranger anxiety. At reunion the infant actively avoids contact with the caregiver. The caregiver tends to be insensitive and may ignore the infant during play. These infants play independently.

Insecure-resistant attachment

The infant is distressed when the caregiver goes and, although when the caregiver returns he/she rushes to the caregiver, the infant is not easily consoled. The infant may resist contact with the caregiver, or may seek comfort and reject it at the same time. These children explore less than other children.

In samples of middle-class American children, Ainsworth et al. found that about 65% were classed as secure, 15% were classed as insecure-avoidant and 20% insecure-resistant.

Main and Solomon (1986) added a fourth type of attachment — **disorganised attachment** — in which there are no set patterns of behaviour at separation or reunion.

Item 3
The Strange Situation: evaluation

When assessing the reliability and validity of the Strange Situation, the following questions should be borne in mind:
- Do infants perform in the same way when retested (reliability)?
- Does the method correlate with other behaviours that signify secure attachment (construct validity)?
- What is being tested? Is the Strange Situation measuring the relationship between the child and his/her caregiver or is it measuring a personality characteristic in the child which might be the same no matter who he/she was tested with?

- Are the Strange Situation procedures relevant in different cultures? The procedures are based on American attitudes and values, for example that 'good' development is promoted by independence. This means that the use of the Strange Situation in other cultural settings may not be appropriate. That said, the majority of studies into infant attachment use the Strange Situation procedures (or some adaptation of them) and the original procedures have been adapted for research on older children.

How reliable is the Strange Situation?

Waters (1978) found 90% reliability when infants were tested and retested between the ages of 12 and 18 months. There was some evidence that stability is lower in 'working-class' families, but this could be explained as being due to the fact that their lives were generally less stable across the period of repeated testing.

Main et al. (1985) conducted a longitudinal study. Infants were assessed in the Strange Situation before the age of 18 months with both their mothers and fathers. When the children were retested at the age of 6 years, the researchers found considerable consistency in security of attachment to both parents. Of the secure babies, 100% were classified as securely attached to both parents at 6 years, and 75% of avoidant babies were reclassified as avoidant at age 6.

Item 4
Cross-cultural variation in the development of attachment

If infant attachment is innate, then attachment behaviours should be similar in all cultures.

Sagi, van Ijzendoorn and Koren-Karie (1991) studied attachment styles of infants in the USA, Israel, Japan and Germany. They reported as follows:

- **American children** — 71% secure attachment, 12% insecure-resistant, 17% insecure-avoidant.
- **Israeli children** (raised in a kibbutz) — 62% secure attachment, 33% insecure-resistant, 5% insecure-avoidant. The children in the kibbutz were looked after by adults who were not their family but they saw few strangers. This may explain why the children were not anxious when their caregiver left but were anxious when the stranger appeared.
- **Japanese children** — 68% secure attachment, 32% insecure-resistant and few insecure-avoidant. It was noted that Japanese children are rarely left by their mother, so the mother leaving during the Strange Situation may have been particularly stressful. Their anxious behaviour may be the result of the mother leaving rather than of a stranger arriving.

- **German children** — 40% securely attached, 49% insecure-avoidant, 11% insecure-resistant. German children are encouraged to be independent and not to be clingy. The high percentage of insecure-avoidant children may reflect the cultural ethos of valuing independence.

Item 5
Van Ijzendoorn and Kroonenberg (1988)

The researchers compared the results of 32 Strange Situation studies in eight countries (involving 2000 children). The findings were shown in the table.

The researchers noted that:
- variations within one culture were 1.5 times greater than variations between cultures, which suggests that any one culture may comprise several subcultures
- although large numbers of children were studied overall, some sample sizes were small. In the Chinese study, for example, only 36 children were used. It may be unsafe to generalise the results to all Chinese infants as 36 children may not be representative of the population.
- the Strange Situation is based on US culture and observed behaviour may not have the same meaning in different cultures. The use of procedures developed in one culture may not be a valid measure of behaviour in another culture.

Country	Number of studies	Percentage of each attachment type		
		Secure	Avoidant	Resistant
West Germany	3	57	35	8
Great Britain	1	75	22	3
Netherlands	4	67	26	7
Sweden	1	74	22	4
Israel	2	64	7	29
Japan	2	68	5	27
China	1	50	25	25
USA	18	65	21	14
Average		**65**	**20**	**14**

Van Ijzendoorn & Kroonenberg (1988): cross-cultural comparison of infant behaviour in the Strange Situation

1 Summarise the procedures in the Strange Situation. Write about 100 words and avoid simply writing out the steps in the procedures.

2 a & b Complete these sentences relating to the Strange Situation by (i) describing how the child might behave and (ii) explaining why the child might behave in that way.

Topic 2: Individual differences in attachments

Answers

1

2a When the caregiver reappears, the securely attached child

b When the caregiver reappears, a child who has developed an insecure-avoidant attachment

3a Complete the mapping of the account of Mrs Brown and Paris onto the Strange Situation. Stages 1 and 2 have been completed for you.

A real-life Strange Situation: Mrs Brown and Paris

Mrs Brown cracked a tooth and needed to go to the dentist. She took Paris, her 18-month-old son, with her. She sat in the waiting room while Paris played happily on the floor. The dental assistant, Jan, had offered to watch Paris while his mum had her tooth checked. So when Mrs Brown left to see the dentist Jan gave Paris a toy train and watched him play. He played happily with the train for several minutes, but then began to whimper so Jan gave him a soft toy to cuddle. After about 15 minutes, Mrs Brown returned and Jan went back to the reception desk. Paris smiled, shouted 'Mum, Mum...' and toddled to Mrs Brown, who picked him up and gave him a cuddle. Mrs Brown had to wait for the result of the X-ray, and as she waited, Paris crawled around the room playing happily with the toy train. When her name was called, Mrs Brown left Paris playing again and asked Jan to watch him while she went to talk to the dentist. Jan went back to watch Paris for a few minutes. When Mrs Brown returned, Paris hugged Mrs Brown's legs and showed that he wanted to be picked up. Jan left, Mrs Brown picked up Paris and gave him a big cuddle and they both went home.

b Relating this episode to the Strange Situation, explain whether you would categorise Paris as having developed a secure or an insecure attachment to Mrs Brown.

3a In **stage 1**, Mrs Brown sits in the waiting room and Paris plays on the floor with the toys. He is relaxed and explores the room. In **stage 2**, the dental assistant, Jan (the stranger), enters the room, exchanges a few words with Mrs Brown and then offers Paris a toy...

b

4 Use your textbook and read Items 2 and 3.

a Describe *two* factors that lead to secure attachment.

4a

b In about 80 words, describe the aims, procedures and findings of one study that used the Strange Situation to look at secure/insecure attachment.

b

c Outline *two* criticisms of research into secure and insecure attachment.
(**Hint:** criticisms may be positive as well as negative.)

c

5 Refer to your textbook and to Item 5 and put the words in these two sentences in the correct order:

5 innate should attachment be in cultures If infant attachment is then (nature) behaviour behaviours similar all. between is cultures If attachment infant learned behaviour then (nurture) behaviours attachment vary should.

6 Refer to the van Ijzendoorn and Kroonenberg (1988) table of results in Item 5.

a Transfer the percentages of securely attached children in the eight countries to the bar chart. (The USA percentage has been drawn as a guide.)

6a

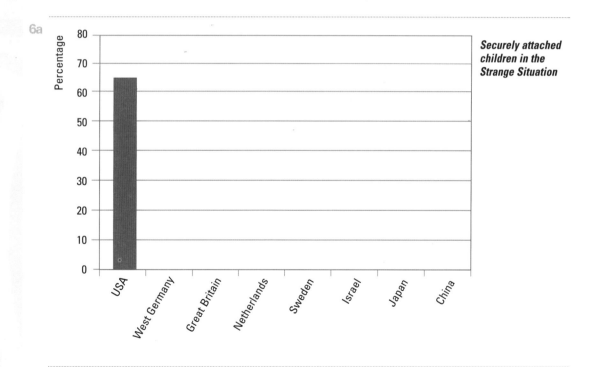

Securely attached children in the Strange Situation

Topic 2: Individual differences in attachments

b Transfer the percentages of insecure-avoidant attached children in the eight countries to the bar chart below. (The USA percentage has been drawn as a guide.)

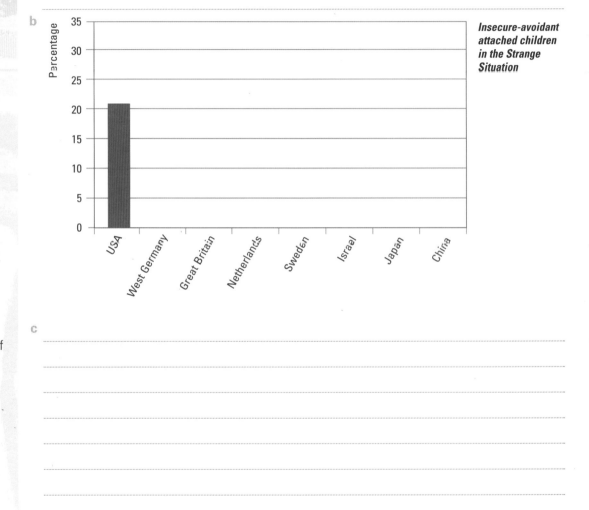

Insecure-avoidant attached children in the Strange Situation

c Your bar charts should show greater cultural differences in the percentages of insecure-avoidant attachments than in secure attachments. Referring to the conclusions of Sagi, van Ijzendoorn and Koren-Karie (1991), explain this difference in the children's insecure-avoidant attachments.

(**Hint:** refer to children in two countries and write about 30 words for each.)

7 The study by van Ijzendoorn and Kroonenberg (1988) is a comparison of cross-cultural studies using the Strange Situation. Read Items 4 and 5 and the relevant sections of your textbook before answering the following questions.

a Outline the findings and conclusions of the van Ijzendoorn and Kroonenberg (1988) study.

b Suggest why children from different countries may behave differently in the Strange Situation.

c Suggest why there may be differences within a country in children's reactions to the Strange Situation.

d Can the Strange Situation procedures be used to assess the development of secure attachments in children regardless of which culture they are brought up in? Explain your answer with reference to cross-cultural research.

7a

b

c

d

Why do infants develop attachments? Explanations of attachments try to account for how and why children become attached to a caregiver. This topic will review two theories of attachment: (a) the learning theory explanation as to how and why attachments develop; and (b) Bowlby's well-known theory of attachment.

Item 1
How learning theory explains attachments

The basic principle of learning theory is that all behaviour is learned. Throughout the early and mid-1900s, learning theory (behaviourism) dominated psychological explanations about how and why early social relationships are formed. The main argument proposed by learning theorists is that the infant's emotional dependence on, and bond with, his or her caregiver can be explained in terms of secondary reinforcement arising from the satisfaction of basic physiological needs such as food and drink. The mother (or caregiver) relieves these needs and thus acquires reward value as the infant learns to associate pleasure with the caregiver.

Based on **classical conditioning**, receiving food gives the infant pleasure, so when the caregiver feeds him or her the infant feels pleasure. Thus an association is formed between the caregiver and food, so that whenever the caregiver is near, the infant feels pleasure — expressed as attachment behaviours.

Based on **operant conditioning**, infants feel discomfort when they are hungry and so desire food to remove the discomfort. They learn that if they cry, their caregiver feeds them and the discomfort is removed. This is negative reinforcement: the consequences of behaviour (crying) lead to something unpleasant ceasing (feeling hungry stops). Thus, proximity-seeking behaviour is reinforced, which in turn leads to the attachment behaviour of distress on being separated from the caregiver.

Item 2
Feeding does not explain attachments: Harlow (1959)

Reread the description of Harlow's experiment with monkeys (Topic 1, Item 3, page 45).

Item 3
Bowlby's theory of attachment (1969)

Bowlby disagreed with the learning theory of attachment. He suggested that social behaviours such as following, clinging, sucking, smiling and crying are innate, and that the function of these behaviours is to bond the child to its caregiver. Bowlby suggested that infants are born with a drive to form attachments and that infants possess characteristics (**social releasers**, such as smiles) that facilitate the caregivers' attachment to them. According to Bowlby, attachment is an **interactive and innate two-way relationship**, in which the caregiver is as attached as the infant. The role of attachment is adaptive as it promotes survival by (a) maintaining proximity between infant and caregiver; (b) assisting cognitive development; and (c) providing the opportunity for learning through imitation.

Bowlby proposed that infants have many attachments but that the one at the top of the hierarchy has especial significance for emotional development. The infant becomes most closely attached to the individual who responds in the most sensitive manner, which leads the infant to have one primary attachment object (**monotropy**). The primary attachment object need not be the infant's biological mother. The child learns from the relationship with the primary caregiver and this relationship acts as a **template** for future relationships. Bowlby called this an **internal working model** (a cognitive schema) that generates expectations for all future relationships.

Bowlby's attachment theory focuses on the interpersonal processes that create attachments, particularly the innate tendency in infants to seek attachment and to elicit caregiver responses through smiles and other social releasers.

In his theory, Bowlby proposed that the development of attachments follows an innate maturational sequence.

This is outlined below.

Phase 1: birth to 8 weeks

- Orientation and signals are directed towards people without discrimination.
- Infants behave in characteristic and friendly ways towards other people but their ability to discriminate between them is limited.

Phase 2: 8–10 weeks to 6 months

- Orientation and signals are directed towards one or more special people.
- Infants continue to be generally friendly but there is beginning to be a difference of behaviour towards one primary caregiver.

Phase 3: 6 months to 1–2 years old

- There is maintenance of closeness to a special person by means of locomotion as well as signals.
- The infant starts to follow his or her caregiver (displaying **separation anxiety**), greets the caregiver when he or she returns and uses the caregiver as a safe base from which to explore.
- The infant selects other people as subsidiary attachment figures but treats strangers with caution (**stranger anxiety**).

Topic 3: Explanations of attachment

1 Read your textbook and Items 1 and 2. Circle true or false for the following statements.

Answers

1a In classical conditioning, the caregiver is associated with food, which elicits pleasure.   TRUE / FALSE

b In operant conditioning, the desire to stay close (seeking proximity) to the caregiver is reinforced because the caregiver feeds the child, which stops the unpleasant feeling of hunger.   TRUE / FALSE

c In operant conditioning, attachment behaviours are learned.   TRUE / FALSE

d In operant conditioning, attachment behaviours are the result of negative and positive reinforcement.   TRUE / FALSE

e Harlow's research found that infants prefer to stay close to caregivers who provide food.   TRUE / FALSE

2 Outline how behaviourists (learning theorists) explain attachment.

2

3 Read Item 2.

a Explain why Harlow's research on monkeys challenges the behaviourist explanation of attachment.

3a

b Describe *one* strength and *one* weakness of the learning theory explanation of attachment.

b

4 Read your textbook and Item 3.

a What are 'social releasers' and how are they important to attachment?

b What does 'maintaining proximity' mean, and how would this help both cognitive development and survival?

c Why is Bowlby's theory described as an evolutionary theory?

d Outline Bowlby's theory of attachment. (**Note:** you will need to be able to describe this theory in about 100–150 words for the exam.)

4a

b

c

d

5 Read through Items 1–3. Complete the table to compare the learning (behaviourist) theory and Bowlby's explanation of attachment.

	Learning theory	Bowlby's theory
Factors leading to infant attachment		
Factors leading to caregiver attachment		
Supporting evidence		
Opposing evidence		
Strength(s)		
Weakness(es)		

Topic 4 Separation, deprivation and privation

In the context of developmental psychology, **separation** is when a child is separated from his/her attachment figure for a relatively short period of time. Adequate substitute care may prevent lasting damage to the attachment bond.

Deprivation is the loss of something that is needed. Maternal deprivation occurs when a child has formed an attachment but then experiences the loss of the mother or other attachment figure. The loss is long term or permanent and the attachment bond is broken.

Privation means never having been able to satisfy a certain need. Maternal privation is when a child has never been able to form a close relationship (develop an attachment) with any one caregiver.

Separation

Item 1
The protest, despair, detachment (PDD) model

Psychological research into the effect of separating an infant from its attachment figure suggests that children react by showing a syndrome of typical emotional behaviours. **Bowlby (1952)** and **Robertson and Robertson (1968)** studied young children, who were separated from their attachment figure (usually their mother); the researchers found there were three stages in the children's separation behaviours:

The protest, despair, detachment (PDD) model

Stage 1: protest During this stage, the child protests at the separation by crying (which may be continuous), calling for his/her mother or caregiver and showing signs of panic.

Stage 2: despair After a day or so, the child appears to lose interest in his/her surroundings, becomes withdrawn, cries less frequently and may eat and sleep poorly.

Stage 3: detachment The child cries less and appears to have recovered, becoming more alert and interested in his/her surroundings. If the caregiver reappears, the child may not show much interest. The attachment bond between the child and the caregiver may be damaged, but most children re-establish their attachment to the caregiver over time, though for some the bond may be permanently broken.

Item 2
Evidence for the PDD model: Robertson and Robertson (1968)

James and Joyce Robertson observed and filmed the responses of healthy young children to separation from their mothers or caregivers. Their intention was to show that the distress experienced by some children when separated could be reduced or even prevented if they were given substitute emotional care. They observed the behaviour of five children, aged 1–2, whose mothers were hospitalised for between 9 and

27 days for the birth of a new baby. The results for two of the children were as follows:

John: 17 months (9 days in a residential nursery)	Jane: 17 months (10 days in foster care)
In the nursery, the system of group care made it impossible for John to find a substitute mother. The nurses did not understand or respond to his attention-seeking behaviour. Under the cumulative stress of separation from his mother, the lack of 'mothering' from the nurses, the strange food and institutional routines, eventually he refused food and drink, stopped playing, cried a great deal and gave up trying to get the nurses' attention. Visits from his father failed to relieve his anxiety. Upon reunion with his mother, John screamed and struggled when she tried to hold him.	Jane was placed in a foster home (the Robertson family home) for 10 days. Food and routines were kept similar to those at home, her father visited her daily and the foster mother was fully available to meet Jane's needs. After the first few days she showed the strain of separation by increased sucking, impatience and resistance to being handled, but she slept and ate well and related warmly to the foster family. Supportive care prevented excessive anxiety, and although she was reluctant to give up the foster mother, Jane's reunion with her natural mother was not difficult.

The Robertsons concluded that:
- the short-term separation had serious effects on John, including possible permanent damage to his attachment to his mother
- the child's ability to cope with separation from the mother is affected by age, by the level of maturity, by the parent–child relationship and by the quality of substitute care

Evaluation and application of the PDD model
Robertson and Robertson showed that many factors affect how well children cope with separation, and that separation may be only one of the factors causing a child's distress. Individual differences in temperament and the quality of substitute care may all contribute to the amount of distress and despair experienced by the child. Insecurely attached children may be more affected than securely attached children.

In the 1950s, it was not uncommon for children who had to go into hospital, or whose mothers were hospitalised, to have few visits from their caregivers. Even in the early 1960s, young children were not allowed as visitors on many hospital wards.

Robertson and Robertson showed that the effects of separation are minimised if:
- the child is introduced to his/her 'new home' before the separation, to familiarise him/her with the new surroundings
- the child's daily routine (feeding, sleeping, toys etc.) is organised to be as similar as possible to his/her familiar one
- the replacement carer talks to the child about the absent mother/caregiver

Maternal deprivation

Item 3
Bowlby's maternal deprivation hypothesis

Bowlby (1953) proposed that long-term maternal deprivation — the loss of the mother figure or other attachment figure — is harmful: 'Mother love in infancy and childhood is as important for mental health as are vitamins and proteins for physical health' (Bowlby, 1951).

Bowlby suggested that continuous 'maternal care' is necessary for emotional and cognitive development (maternal care may be provided by a 'mother substitute'). This is a 'critical period' hypothesis because, according to Bowlby, there is a critical period, before the age of $2\frac{1}{2}$, during which maternal deprivation will affect development and the effects will be permanent.

In sum, deprivation of the primary caregiver during the critical period has harmful effects on the child's emotional, social and cognitive development. The long-term effects may include separation anxiety expressed as 'clingy behaviour', reluctance to attend school, and future relationships may be affected by emotional insecurity.

Item 4
The 44 juvenile thieves: Bowlby (1946)

Bowlby worked in a 'child guidance clinic'. He found that children who had been separated from their mothers experienced emotional problems and that in some cases their emotional development was abnormal. He diagnosed a condition called **affectionless psychopathy** — a disorder involving a lack of guilt or remorse. He thought there might be a link between affectionless psychopathy and being separated from the primary attachment figure.

Bowlby studied a group of 44 children who had been referred to the clinic because they were stealing (the thieves) and compared them to a control group of 44 children (also referred to the clinic) who were not thieves but who had emotional problems. He conducted a series of case studies in which he interviewed the children and their families in order to build up a record of their early life experiences.

Bowlby found that:
- 32% (about 14) of the thieves could be described as affectionless psychopaths
- none of the control group was diagnosed as affectionless psychopaths
- 86% (about 12) of the thieves who had been diagnosed as affectionless psychopaths had been separated from their primary caregiver for at least 1 week before the age of 5
- 17% (about 5) of the thieves who were not diagnosed as affectionless psychopaths had experienced separation

Bowlby concluded that maternal deprivation may lead to abnormal emotional development (affectionless psychopathy).

Item 5
A criticism of Bowlby: Rutter (1981)

Rutter did not disagree with the suggestion that maternal deprivation can have serious effects, but he disagreed with Bowlby's maternal deprivation hypothesis. His arguments were as follows:
- The term 'maternal deprivation' is misleading because 'deprivation' refers to a variety of different experiences and outcomes.
- Even when separation is demonstrably related to psychosocial problems, this does not mean that separation causes poor development. Antisocial disorders are linked with broken

homes not because of the separation involved but more possibly because of family problems that could be the cause of the separations and the later poor development.

- Affectionless psychopathy may be the result of an initial failure to develop attachments, rather than a result of broken attachments. This is the distinction between privation (a *lack* of attachments) and deprivation (a *loss* of attachments).
- Individual differences in children's responses to experiences of separation are important. Research has shown that some children are not damaged by deprivation.

Rutter concluded that deprivation and disadvantage can have lasting effects on psychosocial development; however, there is not one single cause and effect, but rather many factors, which vary in their effects. For Rutter it was important to focus on the following:

- the interaction between children and caregivers
- the links between children's experiences and later parenting behaviour
- the importance of factors *outside* the home
- the factors that enable children to develop normally, despite stress and disadvantage

Item 6
Evidence supporting the maternal deprivation hypothesis

- **Spitz and Wolf (1946)** found that hospitalised children developed serious depression, and if their stay in hospital was longer than 3 months they were unlikely to recover completely.

- **Goldfarb (1947)** compared children who had been fostered before the age of 3 months with children raised in an orphanage who were fostered after the age of 3 years. The late-fostered children had lower IQ scores, were less socially mature, had poor language skills and were more likely to be aggressive.
- **Rutter (1998)** found that Romanian orphans who were adopted by the age of 2 showed an improvement in behaviour by the age of 4 but that children who were adopted later did less well.

Maternal privation

Reminder: maternal privation is when a child has *never* been able to develop an attachment to his/her mother or another caregiver.

Item 7
Three studies of maternal privation

Genie: Curtiss (1989)
Genie was discovered at the age of 13. She had been kept in one room, isolated, beaten and malnourished. Although she was given extensive education, and her perceptual skills were reported to be near normal, her language skills did not develop normally. As she grew up she had a series of difficult relationships with carers.

The Koluchova twins: Koluchova (1976 and 1991)
The researcher studied twin boys who had been locked in a cellar and who had suffered extreme privation until the age

of 7. When found, the children had virtually no language skills. When they were 9 they were fostered in a loving home. By the age of 14 their behaviour and intellect were normal. By the age of 20 they were described as of above average intelligence and having loving relationships with members of their foster family.

The concentration camp children: Freud and Dann (1951)

The researchers studied six orphans who had spent their first 3 years, without continuous adult care, in a concentration camp. They were strongly attached to each other and were afraid of being separated. At first they were hostile towards adults, but eventually they developed normal social and cognitive skills. As adults they were described as being within the 'normal range' of development.

Evaluation points from the above case studies

Although these are all case studies, which makes it impossible to generalise, the differences between the cases are important. The following factors should be considered:

- duration of privation (Genie's was the longest)
- experiences during privation (the Koluchova twins had each other for company, as did the concentration camp children; Genie also suffered physical, social and emotional abuse, was alone and was not placed in a loving foster home)
- quality of care following privation (the twins were adopted but Genie was passed between academic psychologists as a research interest and then placed in an institution)
- individual differences in the temperament and intellect of the child

Item 8
A key study on privation: Hodges and Tizard (1989)

Hodges and Tizard (1989) looked at whether there is a critical (or sensitive) period in which *failure* to make a secure attachment can be shown to affect adult relationships. They studied a group of children from their early days in an institution (children's home) until they were 16 years old. Some of the children were adopted and experienced 'normal' emotional attachments. This enabled the researchers to observe whether early privation was associated with long-term emotional damage.

Sixty-five children were studied. The children had been placed in an institution before they were 4 months old. The 'home' had a policy against the 'caretakers' forming attachments to the children and, before the age of 4, the children had had an average of 50 different caretakers. Thus the children (and care-takers) were unlikely to have formed any specific attachments.

By the age of 4, 24 of the institutionalised children had been adopted, 15 had returned to their natural homes (the 'restored' group) and the rest remained in the institution. The children were assessed then, and again when they were 8 years old, at which time the sample was reduced to 51 children.

By the time the children reached the age of 16, the researchers were able to locate and interview 23 of the adopted children (some of whom had been adopted after the age of 4), 11 'restored' children and 5 children who had remained in institutions. A comparison (control) group, consisting of children matched for age and gender with the children in the sample, was established.

The emotional adjustment of the children was assessed using interviews and questionnaires conducted with the children, their matched controls, their parents or caretakers and their teachers. The data collected concerned attitudes and behaviour.

Findings at age 16
- **Relationships within the family:** the adopted children were as closely attached to their parents as the comparison group, whereas the restored group was much less likely to be closely attached. Restored children were reportedly less cuddly, harder to give affection to, and less involved with their families.
- **Peer relationships:** all the ex-institution adolescents were less likely to have a special friend, to be part of a crowd or to be liked by other children. They were more quarrelsome and more likely to be bullies.
- **Other adults outside the family:** the ex-institution children were more attention-seeking and the restored children were more aggressive.

Summary: the comparison and adopted children were most similar in terms of relationships within the family.

In relationships with peers and with adults outside the family, the adopted and restored ex-institution children were most similar.

Five possible explanations for the results
- The adopted families were more middle class than the restored families — was there a class-related difference?
- Perhaps the adopted children suffered from poor self-esteem because they were adopted, which affected their relationships outside the home.
- Adoptive parents put a lot of effort into relationships between themselves and their children but not between the children and their peers. This would explain why the adopted children had good relationships with parents but not with their peers. Restored children had no special help with any relationships, which explains why they had difficulty in all relationships.
- Perhaps the ability to form peer relationships is especially affected by early emotional deprivation. Therefore, the adopted children were able to recover their family relationships when given good emotional care but the same did not happen for their peer relationships.
- Perhaps the ex-institutional children lag behind their peers in emotional development.

1 Define separation.

1

2 Read Item 1. In the table, describe in your own words the three stages of the protest, despair, detachment (PDD) model.

Stage 1: **protest**
Stage 2: **despair**
Stage 3: **detachment**

3 Read your textbook and Item 2.

   a Describe some of the findings of the Robertson and Robertson (1968) study.

3a

Topic 4: Separation, deprivation and privation

b Identify *two* weaknesses of this study.
(**Hint:** you might consider the sample
and the research method.)

b

c Identify *two* strengths of this study.
(**Hint:** you might consider ecological
validity and applications.)

c

d Can we conclude that separation will
always lead to deprivation? Why or why
not?

d

4 'Mary has been told that her mother has had a road accident and is critically ill in hospital in Paris. She needs to go to her mother immediately but she is worried that while she is away she must leave her 16-month-old son, Michael, in the care of her neighbour, Janine.'

Read your textbook and Items 1 and 2. Write a note advising Mary and Janine on what they can both do to minimise the effects of the separation on Michael.

5 Read Items 1 and 2. Describe *two* possible effects of separation.

6 Read Item 3.
  a According to Bowlby, what is meant by the term deprivation?

4

5

6a

Topic 4: Separation, deprivation and privation

b Explain why Bowlby's maternal
deprivation hypothesis is a *critical period*
hypothesis.

b

7 Read your textbook
and Item 4. Fill in
the table to describe
Bowlby's study on
44 juvenile thieves.
(**Note:** for the exam,
you need to know
one study in detail.)

Researcher	**Bowlby (1946)**
Participants	
Research aim(s)	
Procedures	
Findings	
Conclusions	
One strength	
One weakness	

8 Read your textbook and Items 3–6.

  a Describe *two* factors that might lead to deprivation.

8a

  b Describe *two* long-term effects of deprivation.

b

  c Outline Rutter's conclusions regarding the long-term effects of separation/ deprivation.

c

9 Read Items 7 and 8.

  a Describe what is meant by maternal privation.

9a

  b Explain the difference between maternal deprivation and maternal privation.

b

c Describe the aims, procedures, findings and conclusions of the study on privation by Hodges and Tizard (1989).

Aims

Procedures

Findings

Conclusions

10 Use your textbook and read Items 7 and 8. Outline the findings of research (other than by Hodges and Tizard) into the long-term effects of privation.

11 *Exam practice*

To what extent does psychological research support the view that it is not possible to recover from early privation?

- Write a list of points as a brief plan for this essay. In your plan, identify the psychological evidence you will use and the evaluative points you will make.
- In the exam you would, in about 100 words, describe appropriate psychological evidence (AO1 skills) and then provide about 200 words of evaluative commentary (AO2 skills).

Psychologists are interested in whether daycare has a positive or negative effect on social and cognitive development.

Item 1
Daycare: the debate

Daycare refers to temporary care for a child provided by someone other than his/her parents (excluding school). Daycare can be provided in a variety of ways, usually not in the child's home, by nurseries, child-minders or nannies, but does not include residential care or fostering.

Is daycare harmful?

In 1951, the World Health Organisation (WHO) stated that day nurseries would cause permanent damage to the emotional health of a future generation. They based this conclusion on Bowlby's theory of maternal deprivation.

Is daycare beneficial?

In the USA in the 1960s, daycare schemes were established to improve pre-school opportunities for disadvantaged children. The best-known scheme was a programme called 'Headstart', which was supposed to benefit poor children so they could start school having equal opportunities with their peers.

Double standards?

Kagan et al. (1980) suggested that a double standard was being applied, where daycare was considered good for 'lower-class' children in that it improved their cognitive ability, but not for middle-class children because of the effect of maternal deprivation.

Item 2
Research into daycare

Headstart (USA) was a pre-school enrichment programme intended to improve the opportunities of disadvantaged children. Research found that those who had attended enrichment programmes (in day nurseries) had more advanced cognitive skills than 'unenriched' children from similar backgrounds, but that by the age of 11 these differences had disappeared. In adolescence, fewer Headstart children were on welfare, more were in college and fewer were delinquent.

This programme was large and varied so it is difficult to evaluate, but there did not seem to be any negative effects of intensive pre-school education.

Kagan et al. (1980) set up their own nursery school in Boston (USA), where they studied the effects of nursery care. Close emotional contact was ensured because each member of staff only had responsibility for a small group of children.

The study looked at 33 infants who had attended the nursery full time from the age of $3\frac{1}{2}$ months and compared them with a matched control group of children who stayed at home. The children were assessed for $2\frac{1}{2}$ years on attachment, cognitive ability and sociability. No significant differences were found between the groups but there was a wide range of individual differences unrelated to the form of care. It was concluded that daycare was not harmful.

Item 3
Research into child minding

Child minding is a form of daycare that some suggest should be preferable to day nurseries because it is closer to home care. Research does not always support this assertion.

Mayall and Petrie (1983) studied child minders in London. The study involved a group of children under the age of 2 and their mothers and child minders. The study found that the quality of care varied; some child minders were excellent but others provided an unstimulating environment in which the children in their care failed to thrive. There was no control group, however; it is thus possible that some children cared for at home are equally unstimulated.

Bryant et al. (1980) studied child minders in a middle-class area in Oxfordshire. Seventy-five per cent of the children were described as passive and detached and 25% as disturbed and having poor language skills. Many minders were untrained and rewarded the children for quiet and passive behaviour. Bryant suggested that many minders do not see it as part of their job to form emotional bonds with the children or to stimulate them.

Item 4
Effects of daycare on social development

Does daycare harm social development by damaging attachment bonds?

Belsky and Rovine (1988): the negative effects
Two groups of children were selected. One group had experienced no daycare and the other had experienced at least 20 hours' daycare each week before their first birthday. The children were placed in the Strange Situation to test how strong their attachments were.

The children who had been in daycare were said to have insecure attachment types, either insecure-avoidant (they ignored their mothers and did not mind when the mothers left) or insecure-resistant (they were unsettled when their mothers were present but upset when the mothers left). Those who had not experienced daycare were more likely to be securely attached. It was concluded that daycare has a negative effect on social development.

Shea (1981): the positive effects
Two groups of children were selected. Both were aged between 3 and 4. One group attended nursery school for 5 days each week and the other group attended just twice each week. During their first 10 weeks of attending nursery school, the children were assessed for their social skills. Both groups increased their social skills, were less aggressive and inter-acted more with others. The social skills of the 5-days-a-week group improved more rapidly. It was concluded that daycare has a positive effect on social development.

Comments
Some research shows a negative effect, some a positive effect and some no effect. Many factors may influence how daycare affects a child, including the quality of care, the child's temperament and his/her home background.

Item 5
Effects of daycare on cognitive development

Unless a child has a secure attachment as a safe base, he or she may not develop the confidence to explore. In order to develop cognitive abilities, however, a child needs to experience and explore a stimulating environment.

Ruhm et al. (2000): negative effects on cognitive development

Four thousand children were studied. The cognitive abilities of those who had and those who had not experienced daycare were compared. At the age of 3–4, children who had experienced daycare in their first year were found to have poorer verbal skills than those who had not. Those who had experienced daycare in their first 3 years were associated with poorer maths and reading skills at the age of 5–6. It was concluded that daycare has a negative effect on cognitive development.

Andersson et al. (1992, 1996): positive effects on cognitive development

A longitudinal study followed more than 100 Swedish children to assess the long-term effects of their daycare. IQ tests and ratings from teachers were used to assess their cognitive and social development. Children who had begun daycare before they were 1 year old showed the highest scores at the ages of 8 and 13. Those who had never experienced daycare showed the lowest scores. It was concluded that daycare has a positive effect on cognitive development.

Comments

The Swedish children were in high-quality (expensive) daycare and may have had wealthier families and an enriched home environment. However, Headstart also found that socially disadvantaged children who experienced enrichment daycare did better in education. Good-quality daycare may thus be beneficial.

Many factors may impact on whether daycare has positive or negative effects on cognitive development: how well the staff are trained; the ratio of staff to children; minimal staff turnover to facilitate stable attachments with carers; and appropriate toys and activities.

Item 6
A hypothetical daycare quandary

Omar is 18 months old. His mother has decided to return to work 3 days each week. While his mother is at work, Omar will be looked after by a qualified local child minder whose own children are at school. He will be the only child that the child minder cares for.

Shushila is 18 months old. Her mother has decided to return to full-time work. While her mother is at work Shushila will attend the local nursery. The nursery cares for 40 children between the ages of 6 months and 4 years.

1 Read your textbook and Item 1.

  a Explain the terms daycare, cognitive development and social development.

  b Give *one* difference between daycare and institutional care.

1a

b

2 Read your textbook and Items 2, 3 and 4. Then complete the table to outline *three* differences between high- and low-quality daycare.

High-quality daycare	Low-quality daycare

3 Read Items 2, 3 and 4.

  a With reference to attachment theory, suggest *two* reasons why daycare might have a negative effect on social development.

3a

Topic 5: Critical issue: daycare

b With reference to attachment theory, suggest *two* reasons why daycare might have a positive effect on cognitive development.

b

c Describe the findings and conclusions of *one* study into the effects of daycare on children's social development.

c

d Describe the findings and conclusions of *one* study into the effects of daycare on children's cognitive development.

d

4 Review Items 2, 3, 4 and 5. Read Item 6 and imagine that *you* are going to design and conduct a study looking at the effects of daycare on the cognitive and social development of Omar and Shushila.

a Explaining whose research you would base your study on, outline the methods and procedures you would use and outline the criteria by which you would measure any effects.

b Suggest *one* strength and *one* weakness of your research.

4a

b

5 *Exam practice*

'Daycare can have a positive effect on social development.' Discuss the extent to which psychological research supports this view.

- Write a list of points as a brief plan for this essay. In your plan, identify the psychological evidence you will use and the evaluative points you will make.

- In the exam you would, in about 100 words, describe appropriate psychological evidence (AO1 skills) and then provide about 200 words of evaluative commentary (AO2 skills).